D1159501

the marcel marceau alphabet book

by george mendoza

photographed by milton h. greene

the marcel marceau

alphabet book

doubleday & company, inc.
garden city, new york

Designed by Earl Tidwell

Art direction by Alex Gotfryd

Library of Congress Catalog Card Number 71-127884

Printed in the United States of America
First Edition

for alexandra and matthew

Marcel marceau

is a sea of faces . . .

his body bends

an alphabet of spaces . . .

Awakening

Butterfly

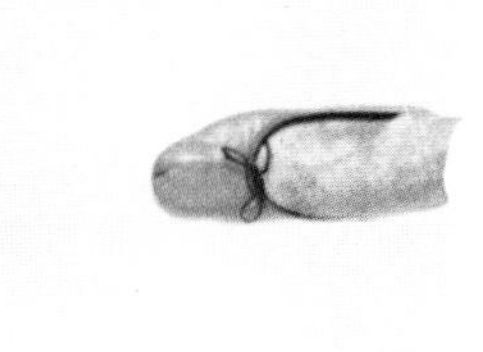

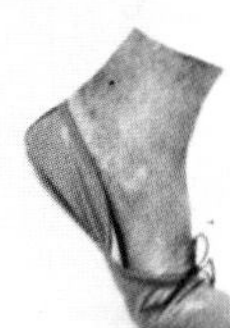

Cage

Dragon

Escape

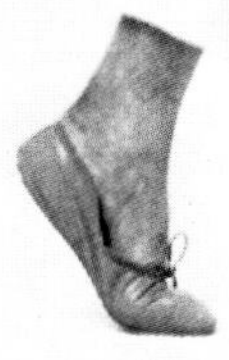

Flower

Giant

Happy

Ice-skater

Juggler

Kite

Love

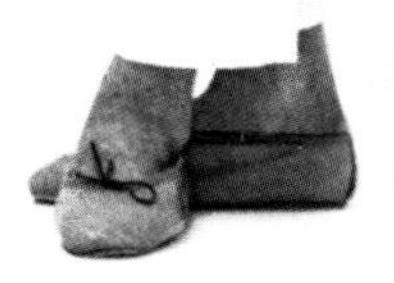

Mask

Narrow

Old

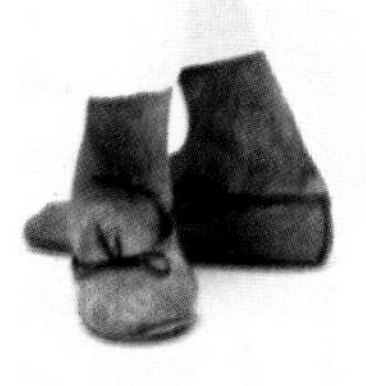

Pull

Quiet

Resting

Snake

Tightrope

mbrella

Vanish

Wonderful

Xylophone

Yawning

z z z z z z z z . . .

Z Z Z Z Z Z Z Z Z Z Z Z Z

. . . he's gone back to sleep.

GEORGE MENDOZA, a native New Yorker, attended the State University of New York Maritime College for two years and received his B.A. degree from Columbia University. Having always lived near the sea, he learned to sail as a boy and has twice crossed the Atlantic Ocean alone on a small sloop from New York to England. A novelist, poet, and allegorist, Mr. Mendoza is also the author of a number of children's books, including *Herman's Hat, The Inspector,* and *The Good Luck Spider*, and is the winner of a Lewis Carroll Shelf Award for *The Hunter I Might Have Been.*

MARCEL MARCEAU, universally acclaimed as the world's greatest pantomimist, was born in a village near Strasbourg, France. His love of mime began in childhood when he used to imitate the motions of people, animals, and natural objects around him. Later he watched such silent screen mimes as Charles Chaplin, Harry Langdon, and Buster Keaton, whom he considered the greatest practitioners of the art. In 1946 he enrolled in Charles Dullin's School of Dramatic Art in Paris, where he studied under Etienne Decroux, who had also taught the famed Jean-Louis Barrault. The latter noticed Mr. Marceau's talent, made him a member of his company, and thereby helped launch his career. In 1969 Mr. Marceau opened his International School of Mime in Paris, in which students from all over the world are enrolled.